IT'S DR. ZED'S BRILLIANT BOOK OF SCIENCE EXPERIMENTS!

An OWL Book
© **Greey de Pencier Publications, 1977**
59 Front Street East
Toronto, Ontario, Canada
ISBN 0-919872-34-4
Printed in Canada
Second Printing May, 1978

*Dr. Zed and his lively team of birds appears as a regular feature in OWL, Canada's magazine for 8 to 12 year olds. Subscriptions to OWL are $6.00 for ten issues, $11 for 20 issues. Outside Canada add $2.00 for each ten issues. Send name, address, postal code and remittance in Canadian funds to OWL, 59 Front Street East, Toronto, Ontario, M5E 1B3.

Canadian Cataloguing in Publication Data

Penrose, Gordon (date)
  Dr. Zed's brilliant book of science experiments

"An Owl book."
ISBN 0-919872-34-4 pa.

1. Science — Experiments — Juvenile literature.
I. Bucholtz-Ross, Linda, (date)   II. Title

Q163.P45   j502.8   C77-001425-9

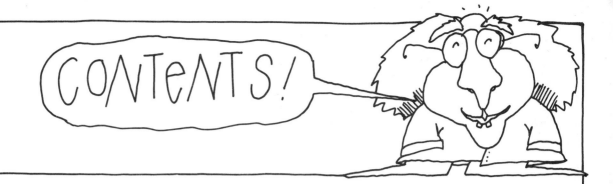

CONTENTS!

FLIP-FLOP 'MAGIC' MOVING PICTURES

ALL QUIET ON THE SET! WE ARE MAKING A DEVICE HERE WHICH WILL FLIP PICTURES AT LESS THAN $\frac{1}{10}$ (ONE TENTH) OF A SECOND! YOU'LL BE SURPRISED AT WHAT YOU SEE!

THIS IS WHAT YOU'LL NEED!

2 blank pieces of light weight cardboard 7.5 cm by 12.5 cm (file cards will do)
crayons or felt markers
glue
an elastic band about 8 cm long when unstretched

Making your "flip flop" cards

1. Draw a dotted line across the middle of each card.

2. Draw a bowl on the top half of one of the cards.

3. Place the blank card on top of the card with the picture of the bowl, and hold both up to a window. Draw a fish on the blank card so that it appears to be swimming in the bowl.

4. Turn the cards back to back, so that the fish is at the top on one side, and on the other side the bowl is at the bottom.

5. Glue the two cards together.

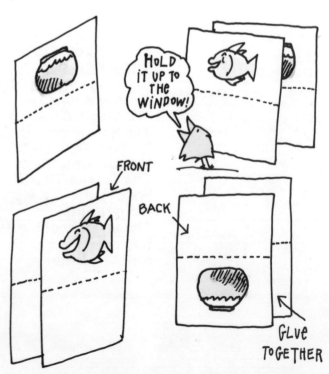

HOLD IT UP TO THE WINDOW!

FRONT

BACK

GLUE TOGETHER

6. Place the elastic band around the cards so that it covers the dotted line.

7. Hold the elastic with the thumb and index fingers of each hand, and with the second finger of each hand flip the card over at least 25 times so the elastic becomes wound up. (If you find this difficult, ask a friend to flip your card).

8. Now hang on tightly to the elastic and let the card go. If you watch carefully you will see the fish *inside* the bowl.

MiNi-AQUARiUM

A GLUB! GLUB!

IF WE MAKE AN AQUARIUM THAT IS VERY THIN, THE POND CREATURES WE PUT IN IT WILL BE VERY CLOSE TO THE GLASS! ...AND THE CLOSER THEY ARE TO THE GLASS THE EASIER THEY ARE TO SEE CLEARLY!

IF THE AQUARIUM IS TOO THIN THERE WOULD BE NO ROOM FOR THE TINY CREATURES!

OUR AQUARIUM WILL BE MUCH LIKE A 'GLASS' SANDWICH! JUST THE RIGHT THICKNESS.

YOU MEAN WE HAVE TO HOLD TWO PIECES OF GLASS TOGETHER? WHEN WE GET TIRED, THE 'SANDWICH' MIGHT LEAK!

DON'T WORRY! ...IT WILL HOLD WATER WITHOUT LEAKING! DR. ZED TOLD ME WE'LL USE 'PRESSURE' TO HOLD IT TOGETHER!

You will need:

2 pieces of window glass 8 cm x 10 cm (Most hardware stores will give you pieces left over from cutting windows, and many will even cut them to size for you.)
masking tape
a 12 cm piece of plastic skipping rope (thin rubber or plastic aquarium tubing)

4 elastic bands (about 4 cm long when unstretched)
2 nails, 2 to 3 cm long
a small block of wood about 15 cm long and at least 3 cm wide
a marking pencil or a crayon
a small clear plastic container (a plastic glass will do)
an eyedropper

Making your aquarium

1. Carefully tape the edges of the two pieces of glass all the way around with the masking tape. (This is so you won't cut your fingers on the rough edges.)

2. Place the piece of skipping rope or rubber tubing between the two pieces of glass as if making a sandwich. Make it form a "U" shape.

3. Stretch the elastic bands across the top and bottom and down both sides of the "glass sandwich" as in the illustration.

4. Tap two nails into the piece of wood about 7 cm apart. Leave 2 cm sticking up.

5. Fit the aquarium over the nails as shown so your mini-aquarium is on a stand.

6. On the outside of one of the pieces of glass draw a small "U" with your wax crayon near the bottom of the "U" inside the glass.

7. With your eyedropper, gently trickle a drop of water down the side of the glass so it comes to rest in the wax "U". If the drop breaks or falls off, gently put another in its place. When the drop is in place you've made a magnifying water lens through which you can watch tiny pond creatures.

8. And now to put something interesting in your aquarium. Collect some pond water in your small plastic container, then with your eyedropper transfer some of this water (along with anything in it that looks interesting) into your aquarium. Observe through your "water drop" magnifying lens.

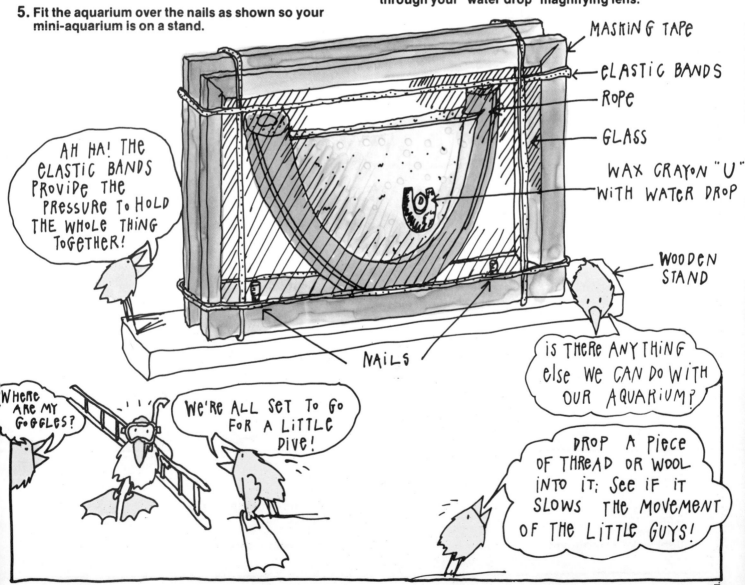

GREAT BALANCING TRICKS

...INCLUDING A BALANCING BIRD!!

You will need:

writing paper	two coins of the same size
a pencil	a thimble
scissors	a needle
light weight cardboard	a bottle with a cork in it

How to make the balancing bird

1. **Fold the writing paper in half and draw the outline of half a bird as in the illustration.**

2. **Cut out the picture through both layers of paper then open it flat.**

3. **Place the bird flat on the piece of cardboard and trace it. Decorate your cardboard bird and cut it out.**

4. **Make two slits in each wing as shown in the illustration. The slits should be about 2 cm apart and long enough so you can insert your coins. Insert your coins in the slits.**

5. **Using the thimble, push the eye of the needle into the cork in the bottle.**

6. **Now balance your bird on the point of the needle. Once you've found the balance point you can put your bird near an open window and it will spin around.**

9

THE GREAT SEED RACE!

YOU CAN TEST ALL SORTS OF SEEDS! EVEN OLD, DRIED OUT WEED SEEDS, ...MILKWEED OR MUSTARD SEED!

AS YOU SEE WHAT PERCENTAGE WILL GROW, YOU CAN ALSO HAVE AN INTERESTING RACE AT THE SAME TIME!

HOW DO WE DO IT??

YOU EACH MAKE A SEED TESTER AND PUT A SMALL NUMBER OF ONE KIND OF SEED IN IT, SAY, BEANS.

You will need:

2 sheets of paper towel, not separated
a ball point pen
a ruler
a glass jar
25 seeds of a kind (any variety will do)
2 elastic bands
water

Making and using your seed tester

1. Fold the paper towels lengthwise to form a long thin rectangle.

2. Measure 10 cm either side of the perforation and draw lines vertically as shown in the diagram below.

3. Join these vertical lines with horizontal lines 1 cm from the fold and 1 cm from the open edge of the towel to form a rectangle.

4. Turn the paper over and measure 2 cm up from the long open edge and draw a line across. In this 2 cm space print "water level". Then turn the seed tester over again so the rectangle faces up. Now you're ready to add your seeds.

5. Slightly moisten the rectangle with water then start placing seeds on it, 5 across, as you roll the towel up lengthwise. Continue placing seeds (5 across) and rolling until all 25 seeds are in the rectangle and the towel is completely rolled up.

6. Place an elastic gently over each end of the roll, moisten the roll with more water and put it in the jar so your "water level" line is at the bottom.

7. Fill the jar with water to the water level line and keep the water at this level. In about 5 days check to see how many of your seeds have germinated.

Note: For every 25 seeds you test you need to make a new seed tester. Be sure to label all your jars with the name of the seeds being tested.

MYSTERY MIRROR WRITING

You will need:

a piece of corrugated cardboard at least 20 cm long
a pencil or pen
a ruler
masking tape or transparent sticky tape
a pocket or purse type mirror
paper

Making your mirror viewer

1. Measure 8 cm from one end of the cardboard and draw a line across.

2. Fold the 8 cm end up so it is at right angles and tape in place.

3. Fold a piece of tape in a loop (sticky side out) and stick the ends together to make a circle. Use it to tape the mirror in place as in the diagram.

4. Tape a piece of paper on the horizontal piece of cardboard in front of the mirror. Now you're ready to start writing.

5. While looking only at the mirror image of the paper try to write the words "Dr. Zed" so they appear *right way 'round* in the mirror.

THE SPECTACULAR ACID and BASE TEST

BEFORE YOUR VERY EYES YOU WILL SEE CABBAGE WATER TURN RED OR GREEN!

CABBAGE WATER IS A PERFECT INDICATOR FOR TESTING ACID AND BASE SOLUTIONS!

IF THE INDICATOR TURNS RED, YOU'VE JUST DROPPED AN ACID INTO IT! IF IT TURNS GREEN, THE SOLUTION IS A BASE! IF THE INDICATOR DOESN'T CHANGE AT ALL, THEN THE SOLUTION IS NEUTRAL!

I CAN'T WAIT TO KNOW WHAT SOLUTIONS ARE ACIDS OR BASES!! ...THEN AT BREAKFAST I CAN SAY 'PLEASE PASS ME THE ORANGE-JUICE-ACID-SOLUTION!!'

THEY'LL THINK YOU ARE VERY CLEVER!

IT'S EXTRAORDINARY!

You will need:

half a red cabbage
a bowl
a knife
hot water
a small jar
a grater
a sieve
an eyedropper
a light-colored teacup saucer
lemon juice

Making the "indicator liquid"

1. Cut the half cabbage in half again, and grate the two sections.

2. Put the shredded pieces in a bowl and add about a cup of hot water. Pack the cabbage down tightly with your hand and let it stand for 2 to 3 hours.

3. When the cabbage water has turned purple pour it through a sieve into a small jar. Your indicator liquid is now ready.

..NOW TO TEST SOME SOLUTIONS TO SEE IF THEY ARE ACIDS OR BASES!!

Testing solutions for acids and bases

1. Using the eyedropper, put a drop or two of the indicator liquid in the saucer.

2. Add a few drops of lemon juice to the saucer and see what color the indicator turns.

3. Rinse out the saucer, and add a drop or two of fresh indicator liquid. Try testing some more of the solutions in the list below to find out if they are acids, bases or neutral. Remember to use fresh indicator liquid for each test.

	ACID	BASE	NEUTRAL
SOAPY WATER			
BAKING SODA MIXED WITH WATER			
STRONG TEA			
MILK			
LEMON JUICE			
OTHERS:			

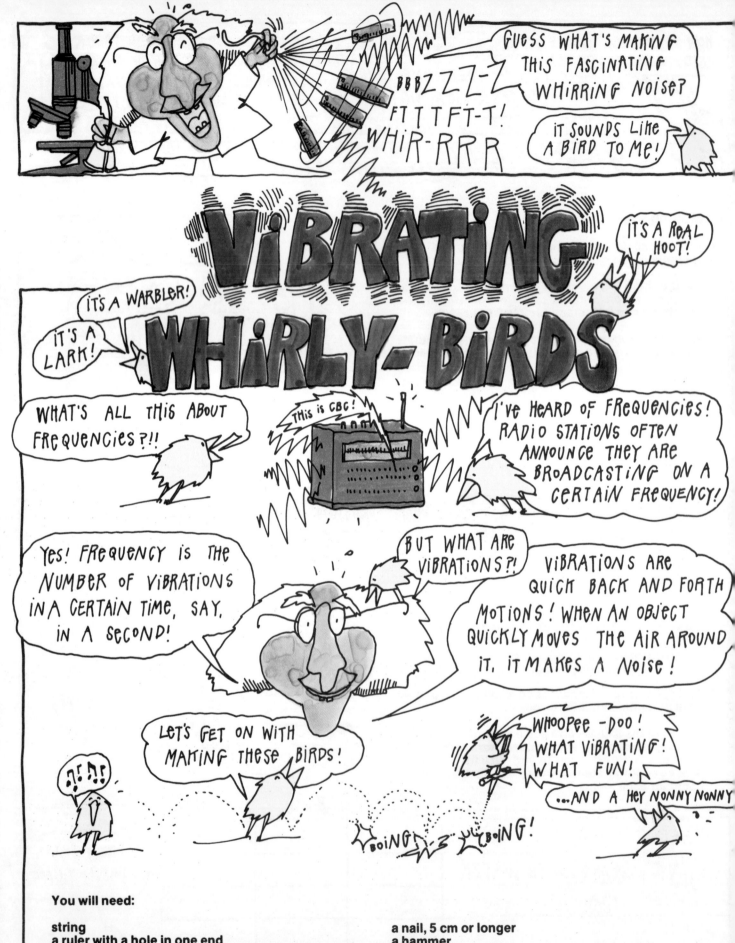

VIBRATING WHIRLY-BIRDS

You will need:

string
a ruler with a hole in one end
a flexible container (cottage cheese type) with a lid;
or a frozen orange juice container with a lid; or a 35
mm film can with a lid

a nail, 5 cm or longer
a hammer
a pen
scissors or tin cutters

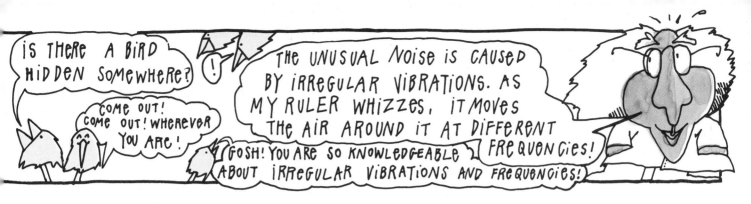

An easy whirly-bird

1. You can make a very simple type of "bird" by threading a string about 90 cm long through the hole in one end of a ruler and knotting it. Whirl the ruler on the string fast over your head (being careful not to hit anything or anybody).

More whirly-birds

2. To make another kind of "bird", put a dot with your pen in the middle of the bottom of the container you are using (the juice can, film can or the cottage cheese container) and gently tap the nail through the dot to make a hole.

3. With your pen, draw a rectangle just slightly over 1 cm wide and whatever length you like on one side of the container. Cut out the rectangle with your scissors.

4. Knot a string and poke it through the hole in the container so the knot is inside. Put on the lid and you're ready to whirl.

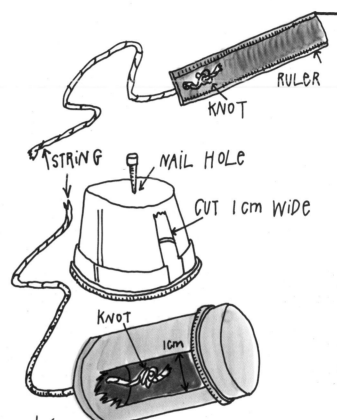

EXPERIMENT BY WHIRLING YOUR BIRD AT DIFFERENT SPEEDS AND YOU WILL GET UNUSUAL SOUNDS!

AS YOU WHIRL YOUR CONTRAPTION AROUND YOUR HEAD IT CAUSES THE AIR TO VIBRATE AT A CERTAIN FREQUENCY! WHEN IT BEGINS TO SPIN THE FREQUENCY CHANFES!

SOUNDS LIKE A WARBLER!

RT-RTTT!

HOOOOTTTZZ

ZZZTTZT!

SOUNDS LIKE AN OWL!

WHAT A CHORUS! HOW EXCITING!

SCIENCE PRINCIPLES ARE OFTEN EXCITING WHEN THEY ARE USED TO HELP US MAKE THINGS WE ENJOY!

You will need:

small pieces of cardboard (file cards)
crayons or colored pencils

Making the "Element Game"

1. Make the game by printing the name of a different element on one side of each card and a labelled picture or labelled pictures of ways it is used on the other.

2. Make as many cards as you like — you can play the game with 10 — but it's better with more. You can look up more elements in a dictionary, an encyclopedia or a mineral book.

3. When you have your set of cards make another set exactly the same and keep the two sets separate. Now you're ready to play.

Playing the "Element Game"

1. Shuffle each set of cards, one set with the name of the elements facing up, the other with the labelled pictures facing up.

2. Put the two sets — one for each player — on a table.

3. One player removes a card off his or her pile. If the picture on top of the one pile and the element on the other match — the race is on — and the first player to shout "Match" wins a card from his or her opponent. If a player makes a mistake and calls "Match" when the element and the picture don't match he or she loses a card.

4. The game goes on in this way until one person has all the cards. Or you can set a time limit. In this case the player with the most cards wins.

You will need:

a soup tin or other metal container
a test tube or a toothbrush container that looks similar to a test tube
10 ml (2 teaspoons) salt
crushed ice
a Celsius thermometer
12 ml (1/8 cup) milk
a couple of pinches of sugar
vanilla
a swizzle stick or other thin stick, about 15 cm long

Making Ice Cream

1. **Put the crushed ice into the metal container so it is about ¾ full.**

2. **Add the salt to the ice and stir until the temperature of the ice is between -8°C and -10°C. If the temperature is not low enough, add a bit more salt and keep stirring.**

3. **Put the milk, a couple of pinches of sugar and one drop vanilla into the tube.**

4. **Place the tube in the metal container and pack ice around it.**

5. **Stir your milk mixture for 10 or 15 minutes, then your ice cream will be ready to eat.**

THAT CHANGE COLOR WHEN YOU SPIN THEM!

1. Begin by tracing a coffee mug on a piece of cardboard to make a wheel about 7.5 cm in diameter. Cut it out.

2. Find the center of your wheel by drawing two straight lines exactly the same length across it. Mark the place where the lines cross.

3. Punch two small holes with the point of a pencil about 9 mm either side of the center point.

4. Decorate both sides of your wheel with one of these patterns. Or make a pattern of your own.

5. Cut a piece of strong string about 1 metre long and thread the ends through the two holes. Knot the loose end.

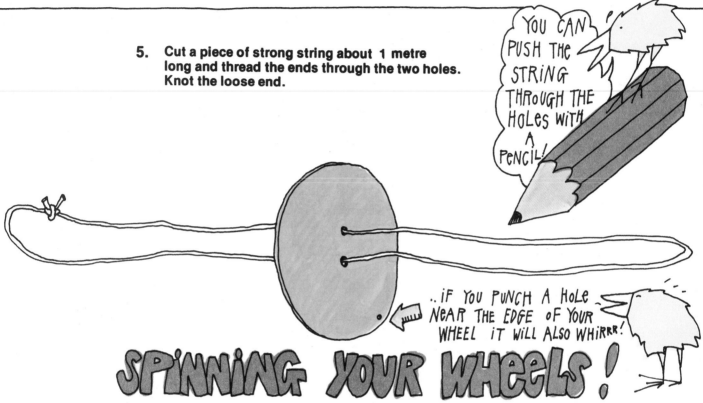

SPINNING YOUR WHEELS!

Wind your wheel up by twirling it as you would a skipping rope. About 20 times will do. Then pull the string tight and see what happens. By pulling the string tight and slackening it you can keep your wheel spinning. The faster you do this the faster it will spin.

GROW-THEM-YOURSELF BIRDSEED PLANTS!

You will need:

a spoon
potting soil
a plastic egg carton
birdseed (a small package of budgie seed would be fine)

transparent sticky tape
white paper
a soup or juice tin
a hammer
a nail, 2 cm to 3 cm long
a "jumbo size" clear plastic bag (about 36 cm by 46 cm)

Growing your own birdseed plants

1. **With a spoon, put some potting soil into your egg carton to a depth of about 2 cm.**

2. **Stick 3 of the same kind of seed to a 4 cm strip of transparent tape.**

3. **Stick the tape with the seeds on it to the inside of the lid of the egg carton. Sprinkle a few of the same type of seeds onto the soil opposite and cover them over gently with more soil.**

4. **Repeat with each different type of seed.**

5. **To make a watering can punch 25 holes in the bottom of the tin with your hammer and a nail.**

6. **Place the egg carton, flattened out, inside the plastic bag. Tie the bag closed. Wait for about 5 days.**

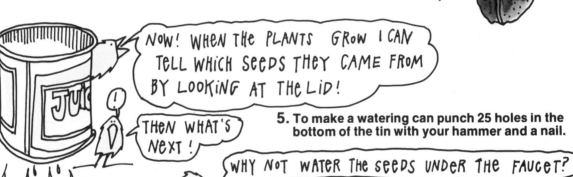

Diver in the Bottle!

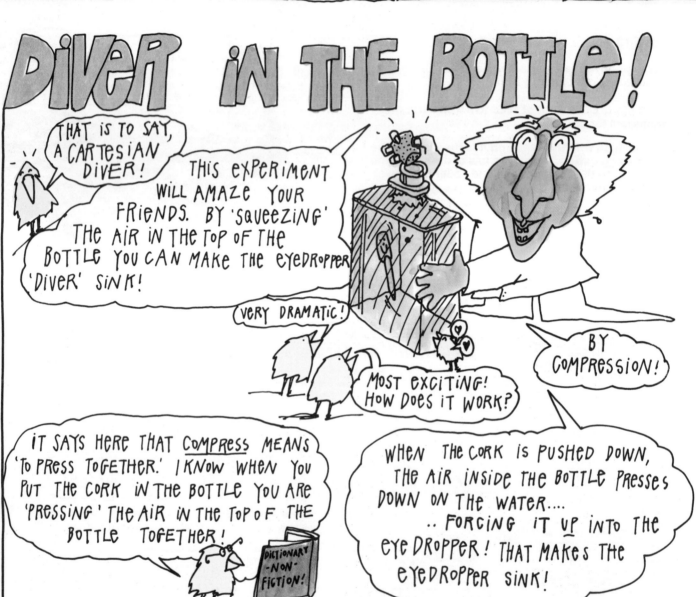

To make your "cartesian diver" you will need:

an eyedropper (with a face drawn on with felt pen if
you like)
a pail at least 15 cm deep
water
food coloring
a rectangular bottle about 20 cm high with a cork
and cap to fit. (The cork must not have a hole, or you
will have an air leak, and the experiment will not
work.)

Making your diver

1. Fill the pail with cold water and add a few drops of food coloring.

2. Fill the bottle to 4 cm below the top with uncolored water.

3. Pinch the rubber top of the eyedropper and plunge it underwater in the pail. Let the eyedropper sink.

4. While the eyedropper is underwater pinch the rubber top again to let in some more water or to squeeze some out. The idea is to get the eyedropper to float so that the top of the rubber part is even with the surface of the water in the pail.

5. Place the eyedropper in the bottle carefully so no water escapes. It should float evenly with the water level. (If it doesn't, put it back in the pail and adjust it so that it floats properly.)

6. Put the cork in the bottle and gently push down on it. The eyedropper should sink. Ease the cork out and the eyedropper will rise.

7. For the next part of this amazing trick, remove the cork and fill the bottle nearly to overflowing with water. Screw on the lid.

8. Grasp the bottle firmly and press the front with your thumbs, the back with your fingers. If the eyedropper is floating correctly (i.e., even with the water line) it will sink as you press the glass. Did you know you were that strong?

And now ... the tapping coin

You will need:

beverage bottle (chilled in the refrigerator)
a coin which fits inside the mouth
of the bottle
a small container of water

1. **Moisten the top of the bottle with your finger and a little water.**

2. **Moisten the rim of the coin.**

3. **Carefully place the moistened coin on the top of the bottle.**

4. **Hold onto the bottle with both hands. Wait ... and see what happens.**

DR. ZED'S 'OFFICIAL' WIND FINDER!

You will need:

a drinking straw
a piece of light weight cardboard (a file card will do)
about 5 cm by 7 cm
a stapler and staples

a straight pin
a small bead
a pencil with an eraser on the end

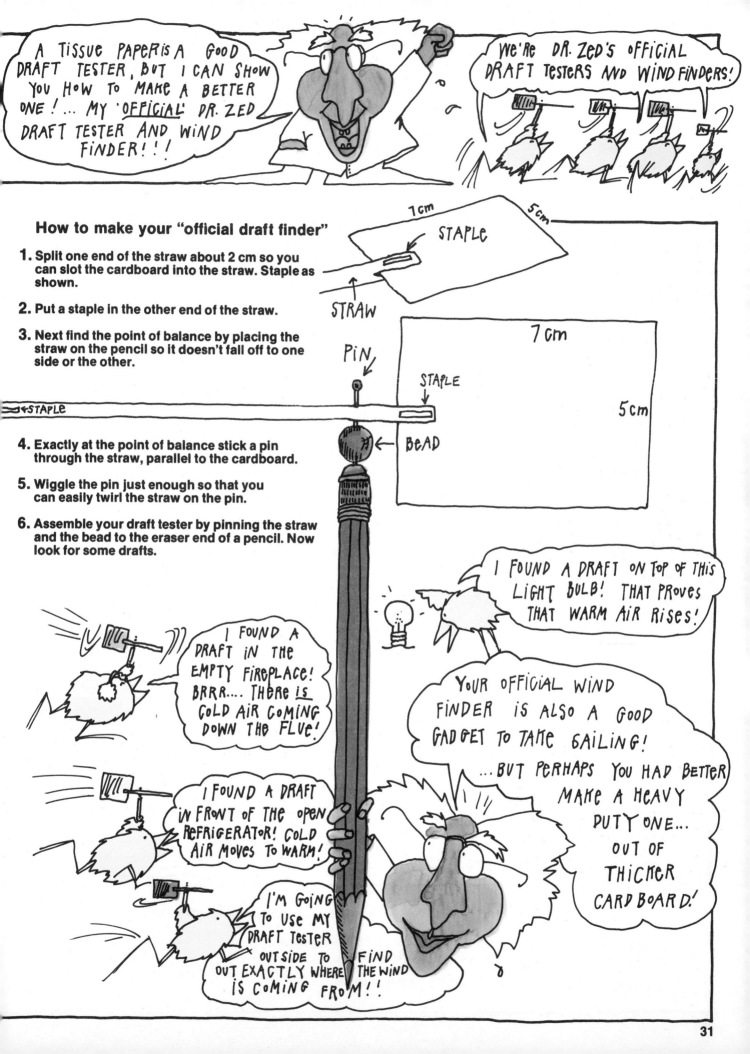

A TISSUE PAPER IS A GOOD DRAFT TESTER, BUT I CAN SHOW YOU HOW TO MAKE A BETTER ONE!... MY 'OFFICIAL' DR. ZED DRAFT TESTER AND WIND FINDER!!!

WE'RE DR. ZED'S OFFICIAL DRAFT TESTERS AND WIND FINDERS!

How to make your "official draft finder"

1. **Split one end of the straw about 2 cm so you can slot the cardboard into the straw. Staple as shown.**

2. **Put a staple in the other end of the straw.**

3. **Next find the point of balance by placing the straw on the pencil so it doesn't fall off to one side or the other.**

4. **Exactly at the point of balance stick a pin through the straw, parallel to the cardboard.**

5. **Wiggle the pin just enough so that you can easily twirl the straw on the pin.**

6. **Assemble your draft tester by pinning the straw and the bead to the eraser end of a pencil. Now look for some drafts.**

7 cm

STAPLE

STRAW

PIN

STAPLE

7 cm

5 cm

BEAD

STAPLE

I FOUND A DRAFT ON TOP OF THIS LIGHT BULB! THAT PROVES THAT WARM AIR RISES!

I FOUND A DRAFT IN THE EMPTY FIREPLACE! BRRR.... THERE IS COLD AIR COMING DOWN THE FLUE!

YOUR OFFICIAL WIND FINDER IS ALSO A GOOD GADGET TO TAKE SAILING! ...BUT PERHAPS YOU HAD BETTER MAKE A HEAVY DUTY ONE... OUT OF THICKER CARDBOARD!

I FOUND A DRAFT IN FRONT OF THE OPEN REFRIGERATOR! COLD AIR MOVES TO WARM!

I'M GOING TO USE MY DRAFT TESTER OUTSIDE TO FIND OUT EXACTLY WHERE THE WIND IS COMING FROM!!

A MIST SPRAYER À LA BERNOULLI

You will need:

a coffee mug or short glass (100 to 300 ml size)
a ruler
a plastic drinking straw
scissors
water
a paper towel

Making your mist sprayer

1. Cut the straw in two. One piece should be 6½ cm long.

2. Fill the glass ¾ full with water and put it on the edge of a table.

3. Hold the 6½ cm piece of straw in the water with one hand. (The cut end should be in the water.)

4. Hold the other piece of straw (cut end in your mouth) at right angles to the straw in the water as illustrated.

5. As you begin to blow move the straw in your mouth *slightly* downward keeping it parallel with the table.

6. You'll hear a high pitch whistle — and then — eureka! — there'll be spray.

7. Short strong puffs will help you achieve a lovely spray. Once you've mastered the technique, you can take your sprayer anywhere.

BELIEVE IT OR NOT, MY CAR HAS A REAL ENGINE!

YES... IT'S SO SILENT, I CAN HARDLY BELIEVE IT!

← AN ENGINE!

THE WONDERFUL WIND-UP SPOOL CAR

THE SCIENTIFIC PRINCIPLE WE USE TO MAKE OUR WIND-UP CAR IS ENERGY!

HMMM... NOW LET'S SEE .. THERE IS ELECTRICAL ENERGY, MECHANICAL ENERGY, HEAT ENERGY, CHEMICAL ENERGY... ...BUT THERE IS NOTHING ABOUT 'ELASTIC BAND' ENERGY!

BOOK ABOUT ENERGY

ELECTRICAL, MECHANICAL, HEAT AND CHEMICAL ENERGY ARE 'FORMS OF ENERGY.' THEY ALL INVOLVE TWO KINDS OF PURE ENERGY- POTENTIAL ENERGY WHICH IS 'STORED' ENERGY, AND KINETIC ENERGY WHICH IS THE 'ENERGY OF MOTION' !!

...IN THIS TRICK WE ARE GOING TO STORE UP ENERGY AND THEN.... LET IT GO!!

AH HA! WE KNOW! WE BEGIN WITH POTENTIAL ENERGY.. AND WHEN WE LET THE 'ENGINE' GO, IT CHANGES TO KINETIC ENERGY!!

?

LET'S MAKE OUR CAR BEFORE THESE BIG WORDS FRIGHTEN ME AWAY!!

YOU SAID IT!!

You will need:

a candle
a knife
a long nail
a cotton thread spool
an elastic band (about 4 cm long unstretched)
a thumbtack
a burnt matchstick

BURN YOUR MATCHSTICK OUT BEFORE YOU USE IT!

How to make your wind-up car

1. Cut about 1 cm off the candle with the knife. Hint: a warmed knife cuts wax easily. Ask an adult to help.

2. Using the nail, drill a hole through the middle of the 1 cm candle piece. Do this very, very carefully or ask an adult to help.

3. With the knife, cut notches on the spool so it looks like a tractor wheel.

4. Put the thumbtack on one end of the spool and loop the elastic over it. Using the nail, push the elastic through the hole in the spool and carefully through the hole in the candle. Thread the matchstick through the loop.

5. Twirl the matchstick about 20 times so the elastic band becomes tightly wound. Now you're ready to roll.

6. Place the car gently on the floor. As the elastic begins to unwind, your car will move forward.

35

INERTIA TRICKS

You will need:

a small ball (a golf ball would do)
a piece of light weight cardboard, 12.5 cm by 20 cm (a file card)
a jar with an opening approximately 1-2 cm wider in diameter than the ball

a piece of cardboard, 2 cm by 20 cm
scissors
glue or sticky tape
a coin
a bottle with an opening approximately 1 cm wider in diameter than the coin

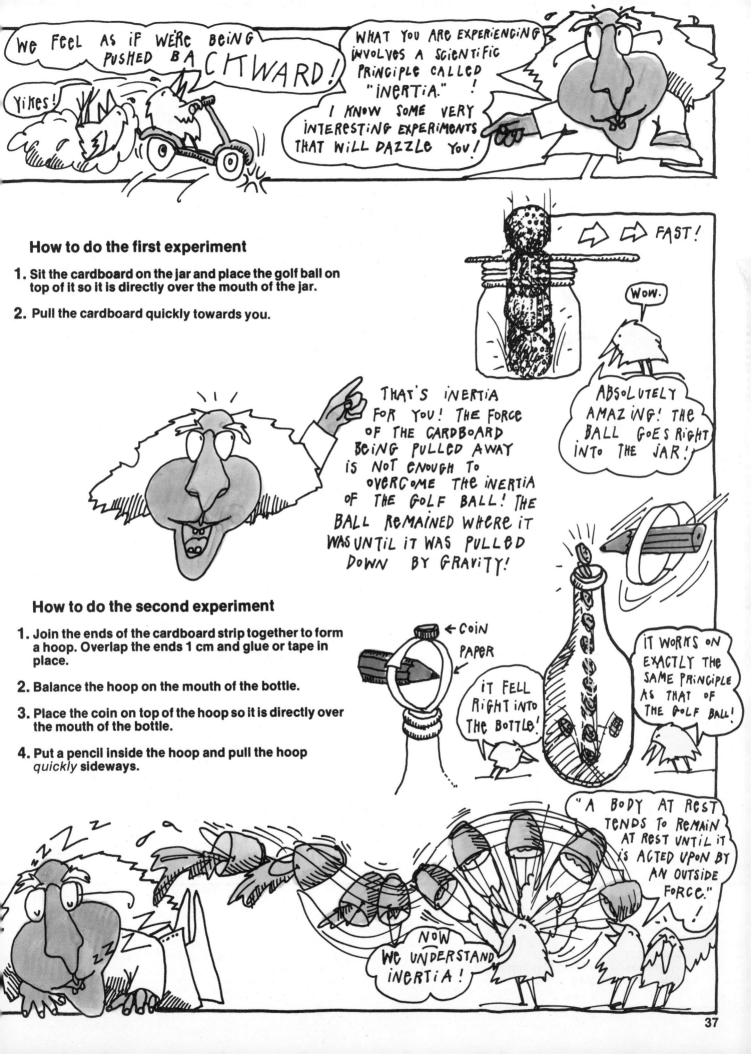

How to do the first experiment

1. Sit the cardboard on the jar and place the golf ball on top of it so it is directly over the mouth of the jar.

2. Pull the cardboard quickly towards you.

How to do the second experiment

1. Join the ends of the cardboard strip together to form a hoop. Overlap the ends 1 cm and glue or tape in place.

2. Balance the hoop on the mouth of the bottle.

3. Place the coin on top of the hoop so it is directly over the mouth of the bottle.

4. Put a pencil inside the hoop and pull the hoop *quickly* sideways.

37

THIS SANDPAPER IS DOING A WONDERFUL JOB OF SMOOTHING THIS WOOD!

HOW DO YOU KNOW WHAT KIND OF SANDPAPER TO USE?

FIRST I USE COARS[E] A "NUMBER 80"; THE[N] A FINER PIECE, A "NUMBER 100." THEN A "NUMBER 220" WHICH [IS] FINER STILL!

SAND SAN[D]
RUB RUB
Hi!
?

MAKING SANDPAPER

WHAT DO YOU SEE?! WHAT DO YOU SEE!! WHAT IS IN ORDINARY SAND ANYWAY?!

SOMETHING WHITE, SOMETHING PINK...

...AND SOMETHING BLACK.

ORDINARY SAND BOX
?

SAND IS OFTEN MADE UP OF TINY PARTICLES OF QUARTZ AND FELDSPAR AS WELL AS MICA OR GARNET. QUARTZ IS THE HARDEST PARTICLE USUALLY FOUND IN SAND. IN THE SCIENCE DICTIONARY CALLED MOH'S SCALE OF HARDNESS, QUARTZ IS RATED #7 ON THE SCALE.

DR. MOH'S BOOK!

HMM.. THE SOFTEST MINERAL IS TALC...IT'S #1 ON THE SCALE. DIAMONDS ARE THE VERY HARDEST. MOH GIVES THEM A #10 ON HIS SCALE.

I THINK I SEE SOME PURPLE BITS IN THE SAND, TOO!

?

LET'S HURRY AND MAKE SOME SANDPAPER OF OUR OWN!

I THINK THEY COULD BE PARTICLES OF GARNET. GARNET HAS A HARDNESS OF 6.5 TO 7.5!

You will need:

newspaper
thin pieces of cardboard (such as filing cards)
white glue (bondfast type)

dry sand (if the sand is from the beach wash it to remove any clay)
wood

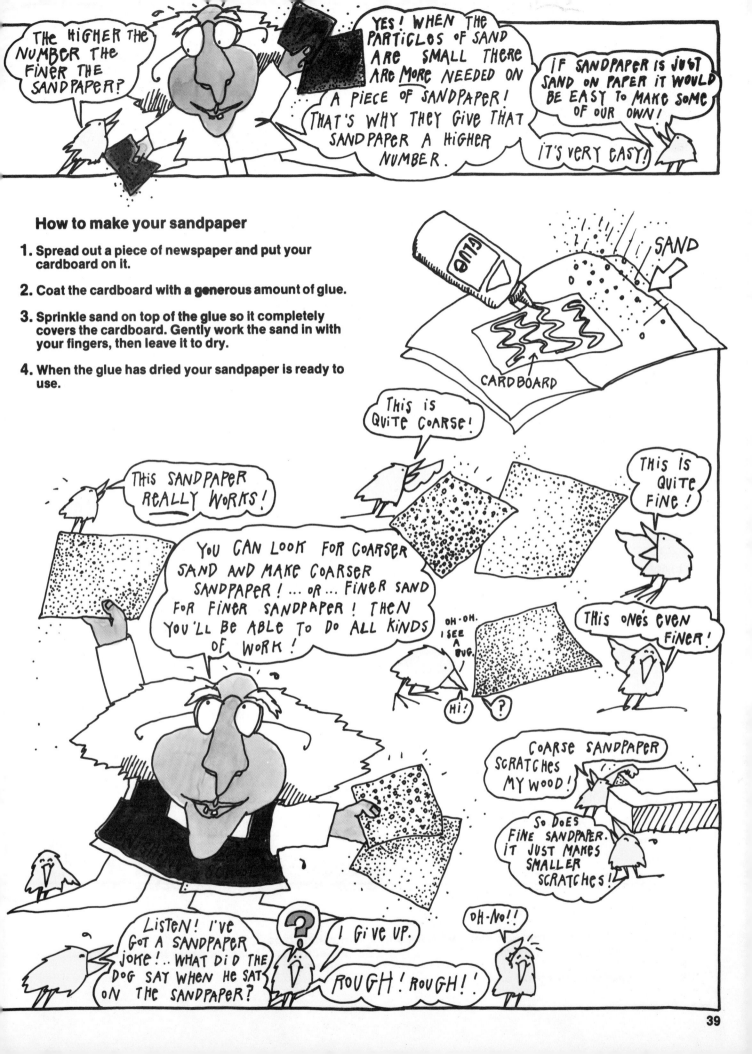

How to make your sandpaper

1. Spread out a piece of newspaper and put your cardboard on it.

2. Coat the cardboard with a generous amount of glue.

3. Sprinkle sand on top of the glue so it completely covers the cardboard. Gently work the sand in with your fingers, then leave it to dry.

4. When the glue has dried your sandpaper is ready to use.

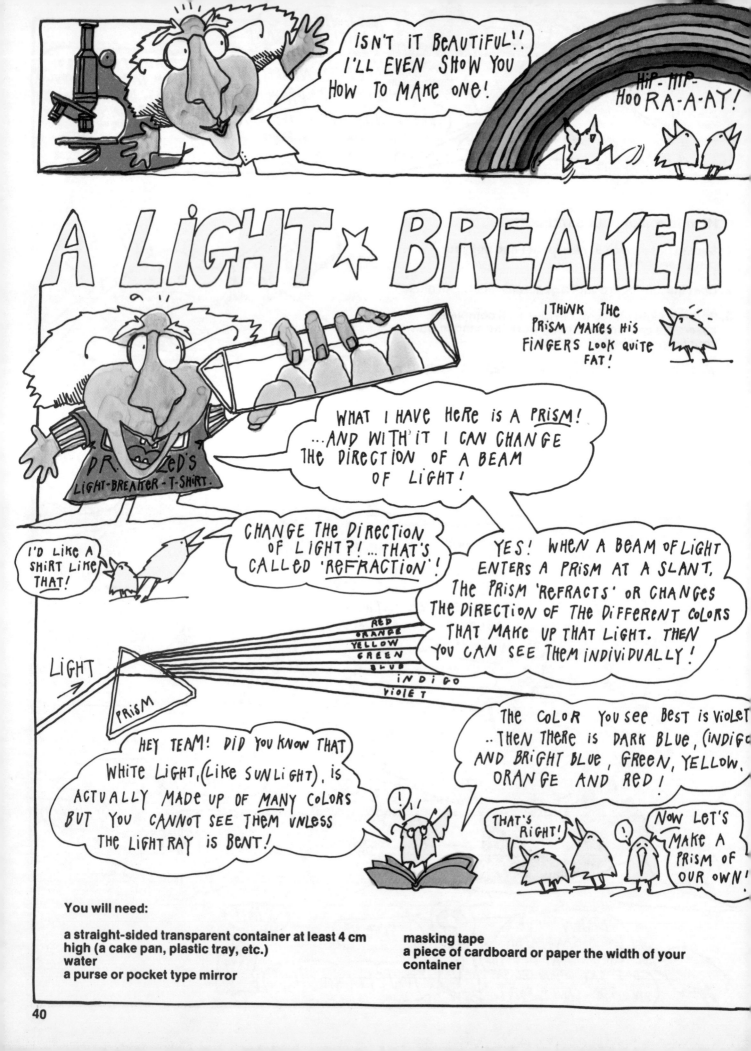

A LIGHT ✦ BREAKER

You will need:

a straight-sided transparent container at least 4 cm high (a cake pan, plastic tray, etc.)
water
a purse or pocket type mirror

masking tape
a piece of cardboard or paper the width of your container

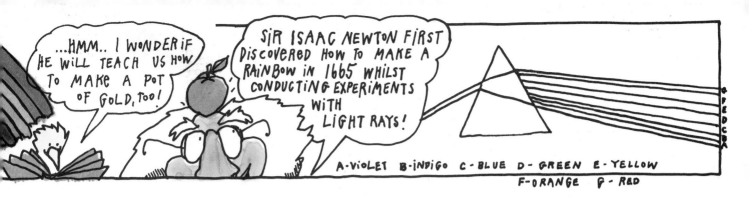

1. Nearly fill the container with water. Place it on the floor or on a table near a window so the sun shines directly on it.

2. Put the mirror in the water with the shiny side facing the sun.

3. Move the mirror until it catches the light and a spectrum (a rainbow) appears on the wall.

4. By adjusting the mirror make the spectrum appear where you want it on the wall. Keeping the mirror at the same angle, lean it against the edge of the container. Hold it in place with masking tape.

5. You can experiment with making the colors of your spectrum more intense by moving a piece of cardboard back and forth above the mirror.

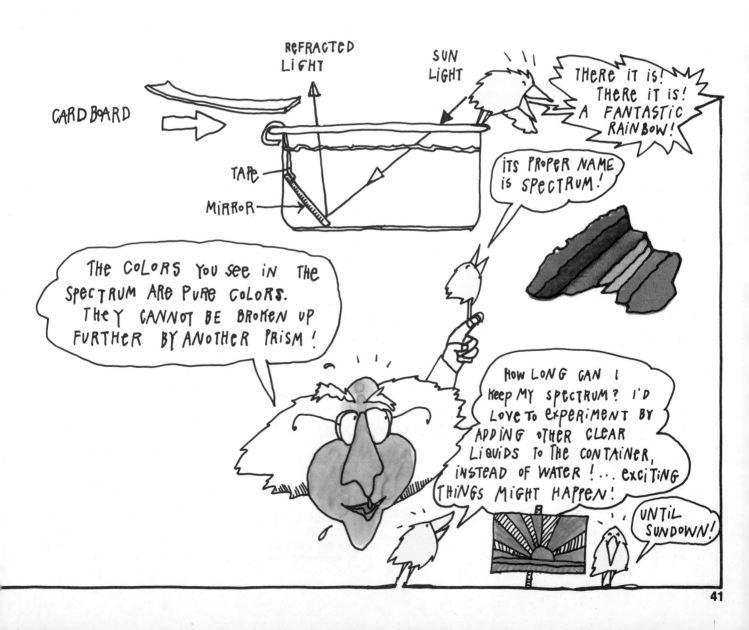

You will need:

a balloon
an eyedropper (glass part only)
2 elastic bands
a nail

masking tape
a knife or scissors
a milk or juice carton (approximately one litre size)
a sheet of writing paper, 22 cm x 28 cm

How to build your "Action-Reaction" boat

1. Draw a small door, approximately 5 cm x 6 cm, on one side of the milk carton. Cut out three sides of the door as in the illustration.

2. Pull the balloon onto the top of the eyedropper and hold it tightly in place with an elastic band.

3. Using a nail, make a hole in the middle of the bottom of the milk carton. The hole should be slightly smaller than the diameter of the eyedropper.

4. Open your "trap door" and push the eyedropper (narrow end first) out through the hole in the bottom of the carton until 3 cm sticks out. (The rest of the eyedropper with the balloon attached will be inside the milk carton.) Place some tape around the eyedropper where it sticks out of the carton so that the eyedropper will not slide back and forth.

5. Close the trap door and place an elastic band around the outside of the carton to hold the door shut. You have made your "engine". Now to make your hull.

6. Use the writing paper to make a "hull" for your milk carton as in the illustration. Staple one end of the hull to form the bow. Place the engine in the folded paper hull so the trap door is on one side.

7. To make your rocket engine work, inflate the balloon by blowing into the eyedropper. While holding your finger over the end of the eyedropper to keep the air inside the balloon, place your boat in a bathtub or large sink filled with water. Remove your finger and away she'll go!

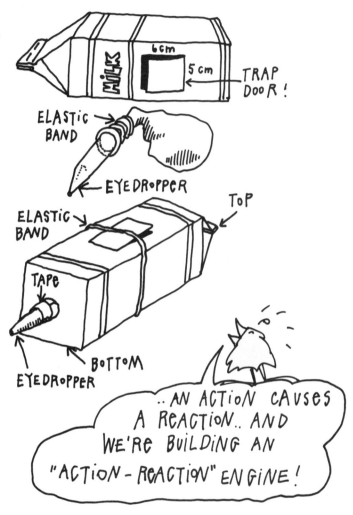

43

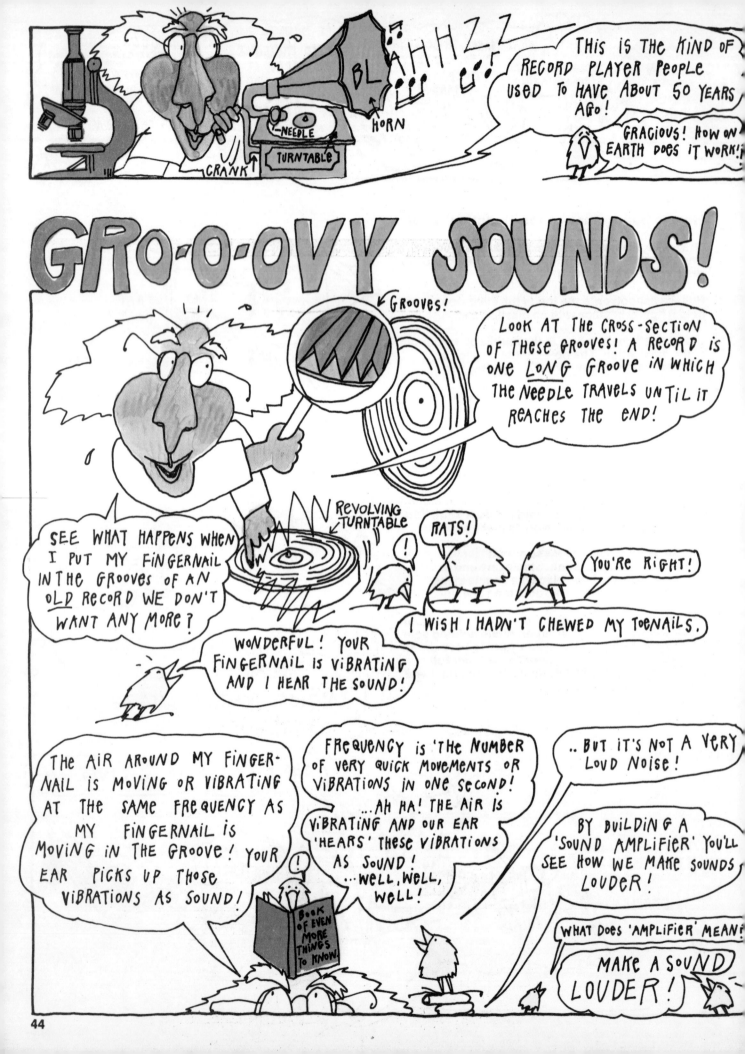

THIS IS THE KIND OF RECORD PLAYER PEOPLE USED TO HAVE ABOUT 50 YEARS AGO!

GRACIOUS! HOW ON EARTH DOES IT WORK!

HORN
NEEDLE
TURNTABLE
CRANK

GRO-O-OVY SOUNDS!

Grooves!

LOOK AT THE CROSS-SECTION OF THESE GROOVES! A RECORD IS ONE LONG GROOVE IN WHICH THE NEEDLE TRAVELS UNTIL IT REACHES THE END!

REVOLVING TURNTABLE

SEE WHAT HAPPENS WHEN I PUT MY FINGERNAIL IN THE GROOVES OF AN OLD RECORD WE DON'T WANT ANY MORE?

RATS!

YOU'RE RIGHT!

I WISH I HADN'T CHEWED MY TOENAILS.

WONDERFUL! YOUR FINGERNAIL IS VIBRATING AND I HEAR THE SOUND!

THE AIR AROUND MY FINGERNAIL IS MOVING OR VIBRATING AT THE SAME FREQUENCY AS MY FINGERNAIL IS MOVING IN THE GROOVE! YOUR EAR PICKS UP THOSE VIBRATIONS AS SOUND!

FREQUENCY IS 'THE NUMBER OF VERY QUICK MOVEMENTS OR VIBRATIONS IN ONE SECOND! ...AH HA! THE AIR IS VIBRATING AND OUR EAR 'HEARS' THESE VIBRATIONS AS SOUND! ...WELL, WELL, WELL!

.. BUT IT'S NOT A VERY LOUD NOISE!

BY BUILDING A 'SOUND AMPLIFIER' YOU'LL SEE HOW WE MAKE SOUNDS LOUDER!

BOOK OF EVEN MORE THINGS TO KNOW

WHAT DOES 'AMPLIFIER' MEAN?

MAKE A SOUND LOUDER!

44

You CAN SEE EXACTLY HOW it WORKS BY MAKING AN AMPLIFIER OF YOUR OWN WHICH WORKS IN A SIMILAR WAY TO THAT HORN!

WE CAN TRY IT OUT ON AN OLD RECORD!

...AND WE'LL LEARN ABOUT SOUND AMPLIFICATION, TOO!

You will need:

straight pins
a piece of writing paper, 4 cm by 8 cm
a plastic cottage cheese or yoghurt container
an old record (important: do not use a good record as this experiment will damage it)
a record player

Making a sound amplifier

Attach a pin to the writing paper and hold it on a rotating record as in the diagram. Angle it slightly until you hear a sound.

AA-LAAAH

THERE IS A NOISE BUT IT'S NOT VERY LOUD!

Making a better sound amplifier

Push a pin through the bottom of your plastic container as near to the middle as possible. Hold the container so that the pin touches the rotating record and see what happens.

AA-LA

BECAUSE THE PAPER VIBRATES IT MAKES THE AIR AROUND IT VIBRATE AT THE SAME FREQUENCY AND THAT MAKES A NOISE!

READ ON TO SEE HOW TO MAKE AN EVEN LOUDER NOISE!

CURT

THE SOUND IS LOUDER NOW BECAUSE THE PLASTIC CONTAINER HAS A GREATER SURFACE TO VIBRATE! THE AIR AROUND IT VIBRATES AT THE SAME FREQUENCY AND THESE VIBRATIONS TRAVEL THROUGH THE AIR TO OUR EARS.

WITH THIS HUGE PIECE OF PAPER YOU CAN MAKE A VERY LARGE AMPLIFIER!

A VERY LARGE AMPLIFIER.

TAPE

PIN

YOU MAKE IT BY ROLLING A BIG SHEET OF PAPER AND TAPING IT IN A CONE. STICK A PIN THROUGH THE END!

PAPER CONE

THE MAGIC DRINKING STRAW FLUTE !

You will need:

a drinking straw (paper will do but plastic works best). If you use a straw with a diameter at least this big, ◯ , you'll find your instrument easier to play.
ruler
scissors

How to make your musical instrument

1. If your straw is paper, flatten 3 cm of one end between your finger and thumb. If it is plastic, flatten 3 cm at one end with a ruler, back and forth.

2. From a point 1 cm from the end of the flattened end of the straw make two cuts as illustrated. You've just made your "reeds".

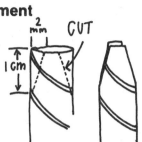

3. To make a noise, put the reed end of your straw well inside your mouth so your lips do not touch the reeds. Blow as hard as you can.

4. Did you get a sound? If not, move the straw even further into your mouth. Blow again. Harder!

5. Still no sound? Take the straw out of your mouth and press the reeds with a ruler until they start to curl up a bit. If your instrument still doesn't work cut the reeds off, throw them away and start over again.

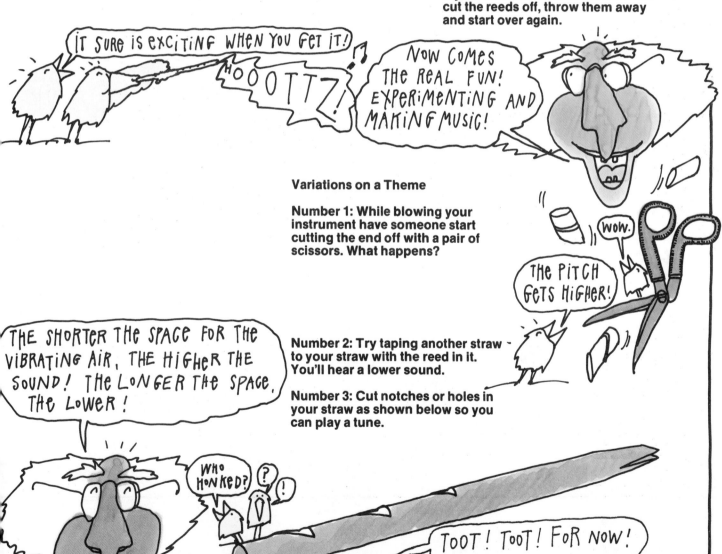

Variations on a Theme

Number 1: While blowing your instrument have someone start cutting the end off with a pair of scissors. What happens?

Number 2: Try taping another straw to your straw with the reed in it. You'll hear a lower sound.

Number 3: Cut notches or holes in your straw as shown below so you can play a tune.

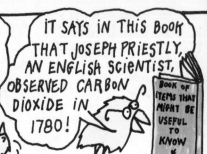

You will need:

scissors
a plastic drinking straw
a clean jar (approximately 256 ml or 9 ounces) with a tight fitting lid
a nail

a hammer
a candle at least 12 cm long and a candle holder
vinegar
baking soda

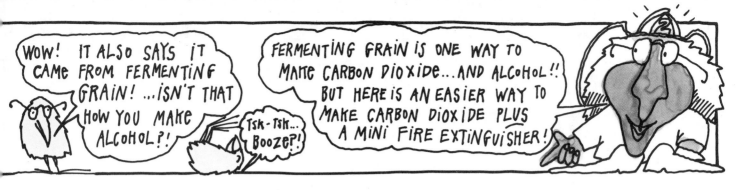

WOW! IT ALSO SAYS IT CAME FROM FERMENTING GRAIN! ...ISN'T THAT HOW YOU MAKE ALCOHOL?!

Tsk-Tsk... Booze?!

FERMENTING GRAIN IS ONE WAY TO MAKE CARBON DIOXIDE...AND ALCOHOL!! BUT HERE IS AN EASIER WAY TO MAKE CARBON DIOXIDE PLUS A MINI FIRE EXTINGUISHER!

Making and using your fire extinguisher

1. Cut a piece of drinking straw 6 cm long.

2. Remove the lid from the jar and punch a hole the same diameter as the straw down through the middle of the lid with the nail and hammer.

3. Push the 6 cm straw down through the hole until 2 cm of straw sticks out.

4. Use the nail to push the rough edges around the hole on the underside of the lid against the straw. This will hold it firmly in place.

5. Light a candle and hold it in one hand. Holding the lid in the other, carefully angle the candle and the lid so the wax drips on the area surrounding the straw and seals the hole tightly. Blow out the candle.

6. Fill the jar one-third full of vinegar.

7. Add 2 ml (½ teaspoon) of baking soda then *quickly* screw the lid on the jar.

8. Now your fire extinguisher is ready, and you can light your candle again.

9. To put out the flame, point your fire extinguisher slightly downwards towards it. (If liquid starts to spurt out, hold your fire extinguisher upright for a few seconds then try again). The invisible gas (the CO_2) that rushes out through the straw will put out the flame.

WAX

FIZZ

VINEGAR AND BAKING SODA

CO_2

IMPORTANT! BEFORE YOU LIGHT YOUR CANDLE, GET AN ADULT TO WATCH!

WOULD YOU BELIEVE IT?!

IT IS AMAZING!

BY ADDING MORE BAKING SODA YOU CAN RECHARGE YOUR FIRE EXTINGUISHER UP TO 3 TIMES!

LISTEN! I'VE GOT A RIDDLE THAT GOES WITH THIS EXPERIMENT!! ...WHAT CAN YOU NOT SEE THAT PUTS OUT A FLAME?!!

WIND!

YOU MEAN ...AFTER DOING ALL THIS, YOU'RE GOING TO TELL ME THAT WIND IS THE ANSWER??! ...WHY.. IT'S CO_2!

...OF COURSE! I KNEW IT ALL ALONG!

Tee-Hee!

SURFACE TENSION TRICKS

...OR HOW TO AMAZE YOUR FRIENDS WITH A SIMPLE GLASS OF WATER!

You will need:

2 transparent containers such as juice glasses (approximate capacity 180 ml)
a towel
water with a few drops of food coloring added

a cup or other small container
an eyedropper
coins

Setting up your surface tension tricks

1. Place one of the glasses on a paper towel and fill to the very top with water.

2. Partially fill the cup with colored water, then transfer the colored water to the glass drop by drop with the eyedropper. Count the drops as you do this.

3. After 50 drops or so, observe the glass from the side. You will see that the water is beginning to "pile up."

4. Keep adding drops until you see the paper towel getting wet from the water trickling down the side of the glass.

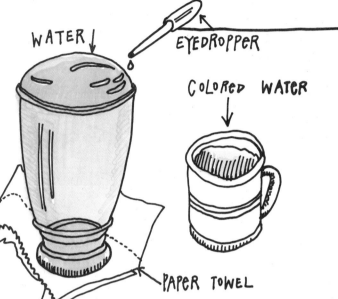

WATER

EYEDROPPER

COLORED WATER

PAPER TOWEL

DID YOU GET 100 DROPS IN?

99.. 100 ! AND STILL GOING STRONG!

IF YOU THINK ADDING 100 OR SO DROPS TO A FULL GLASS OF WATER IS INCREDIBLE, TRY THIS NEXT TRICK! YOU ADD MANY COINS TO AN ALREADY FULL GLASS OF WATER !!

THE SURFACE TENSION IS WHAT KEEPS THE WATER FROM SPILLING! IF YOU WATCH YOUR GLASS FROM THE SIDE AS YOU PUSH A COIN THROUGH THIS SURFACE 'SKIN', YOU CAN ACTUALLY SEE THE SURFACE 'SKIN' RISE AND LOWER!

5. For your next trick, fill your other glass to the very top with colored water. Gently drop coins edgewise into the water one at a time.

6. Ask your friends to guess how many can be added before the water overflows. You'll be amazed — and so will they!

HOW MANY! HOW MANY DO YOU THINK THERE ARE!?

WHAT A TRICK!

You will need:

paper towel; a ruler; a pencil; a small clear plastic sandwich bag; a stapler or straight pins; masking tape; a ballpoint pen; three different seeds (radish, corn, beans or any annual vegetable or flower); water; tacks.

THE EXPERIMENT!

IT'S A MINI-GREENHOUSE!

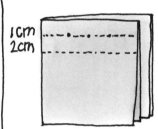

1. Fold the paper towel into four. Draw two lines across the top. Punch three small holes as shown.

2. Fold the paper twice along the lines to make a trough.

1. Fold the paper towel into four. Draw two lines across the top. Punch three small holes as shown.

2. Fold the paper twice along the lines to make a trough.

3. Put the towel into the plastic bag. Make sure the trough is still folded, then staple its edges shut *through* the bag.

4. Put masking tape on the front of the bag above and below the towel. Then draw lines every 4 cm across the bag with a ballpoint pen.

5. Put three different seeds in the trough, one above each hole. Water the towel until it is soaking wet. Put two more staples on either side of the centre hole so that you have made three pockets. Write the date and names of each seed on the masking tape. Tack your mini-greenhouse up on a notice-board or tape it to your wall.

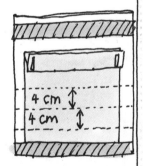

ONCE THE ROOTS HAVE GROWN TO 4 cm TURN YOUR MINI-GREENHOUSE UPSIDEDOWN AND WAIT A FEW DAYS TO SEE WHAT HAPPENS! THEN TURN YOUR GREENHOUSE SIDEWAYS AND SEE WHAT HAPPENS NEXT!

THE SCREEN-THAT-HOLDS-WATER TRICK!

You will need:

screening, the squares of which are less than 2 mm apart (plastic screening is easier to work with than wire)
a "Mason" type jar with metal "ring" lid
pencil
scissors
water
a pail or bucket
a toothpick

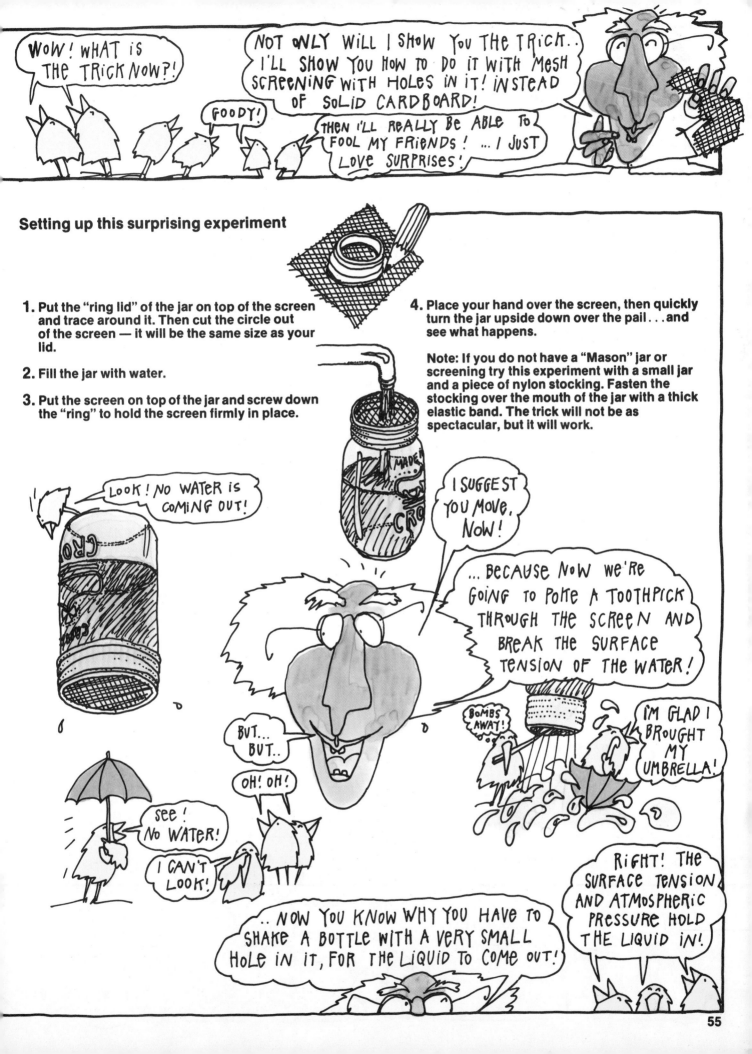

Setting up this surprising experiment

1. Put the "ring lid" of the jar on top of the screen and trace around it. Then cut the circle out of the screen — it will be the same size as your lid.

2. Fill the jar with water.

3. Put the screen on top of the jar and screw down the "ring" to hold the screen firmly in place.

4. Place your hand over the screen, then quickly turn the jar upside down over the pail...and see what happens.

Note: If you do not have a "Mason" jar or screening try this experiment with a small jar and a piece of nylon stocking. Fasten the stocking over the mouth of the jar with a thick elastic band. The trick will not be as spectacular, but it will work.

You will need:
a soft plastic pail (25 cm in diameter is a good size); clear plastic wrap from the dry cleaners *(be sure to keep it away from young brothers and sisters)*; **four elastic bands knotted together in a circle; a sharp kitchen knife; a ballpoint pen or felt-tip pen.**

THE WATER LENS!

Take the handle off your pail. Draw three evenly spaced circles (big enough to put your hands through) on the outside of the pail. Leave at least 4 cm of pail at the top and bottom of each circle. Now ask an adult to cut out the circles.

Cut a piece of clear plastic big enough to cover the top of the pail with a 15 cm lap-over all round.

Put the plastic *loosely* over the top of the pail and keep it in place with the rubber bands. Press down gently on the plastic so that it sags into the bucket. Take the pail outside – you'll need plenty of daylight for this experiment.

Slowly pour lukewarm water onto the plastic. Add as much as you can without overflowing. The plastic

should sag at least 10 cm below the rim of the pail. You have now made a *convex water lens!*

Put objects into your pail through the cut-out holes, then look at them through the lens. You'll be amazed!

DID YOU EVER NOTICE HOW EVERYONE IS DIFFERENT? PEOPLE HAVE DIFFERENT HAIR, EYES, NOSES, MOUTHS AND COME IN MANY SHAPES AND SIZES!

OH YES! ESPECIALLY FEET!

?

FINGERPRINTS

SHERLOCK HOLMES... MOVE OVER!

EVERBODY'S FINGERPRINTS ARE DIFFERENT! IN THIS WHOLE WORLD THERE IS NOBODY ELSE WITH FINGERPRINTS EXACTLY THE SAME AS YOURS!

YOU MEAN THAT THERE ARE OVER 4 BILLION DIFFERENT SETS OF FINGERPRINTS OUT THERE?! ...GEE! WHAT ABOUT TOES?

I'M GOING TO LET YOU IN ON SHERLOCK HOLMES SECRET OF SUCCESS — HOW TO LIFT FINGERPRINTS FROM GLASSES AND OTHER SHINY SURFACES. BUT FIRST YOU MUST MAKE YOURSELF A FINGERPRINT FILE!

WOW.

NICE.

MAKING A FINGERPRINT FILE:

You will need: a stamp pad and white paper

Have your friends and family press their fingers one at a time onto the ink pad and then onto the paper. If there is too much ink the first time, have them make a second or third print without using any more ink.

Put the "suspects'" names beside their fingerprints. When you study these prints you'll find that the patterns are one of two types: whorls or loops. Now you're ready to be a sleuth ...

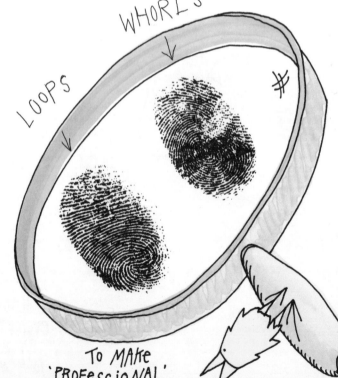

WHORLS

LOOPS

TO MAKE 'PROFESSIONAL' RCMP-STYLE PRINTS, VERY SLOWLY ROLL YOUR FINGERTIP ON THE PAPER!

THE FINGERPRINT SLEUTH-KIT

You will need:

a soft (HB, 2B) lead pencil
an emery board or fine sandpaper
a pencil sharpener
a clean cup
a small brush
wide clear **sticky tape**
Kleenex
white paper
newspaper

And now to gather the evidence ...

First: **Rub the tip of your pencil on the emery board or sandpaper and collect the black dust (called "graphite") in the cup. Then re-sharpen the pencil and repeat until you have enough graphite to cover the bottom of the cup.**

Second: **Pick up the used glass with the Kleenex and examine it for fingerprints.**

Third: **Place the glass on a sheet of newspaper. Dip your brush into the graphite powder and gently dust one of the fingerprints.**

Fourth: **Blow off the excess powder and then cover the fingerprints with a short piece of the tape.**

Fifth: **Peel the tape off very slowly and stick it down on the white paper. Now you have a copy of the culprit's fingerprint!**

I'LL BET YOU DIDN'T KNOW THAT FRESH VEGETABLES GROW WITH WATER IN THEM! ..AND THAT SOME VEGETABLES HAVE MORE WATER THAN OTHERS!

COOK

COOK! COOK!

THE MYSTERY OF THE EVAPORATING VEG.

THAT MEANS VEGETABLES!

HOW CAN WE FIND THE AMOUNT OF WATER IN VEGETABLES? I CAN'T SEE ANY.

PERHAPS WE COULD LEAVE THEM TO SHRIVEL UP?!

LEAVING VEGETABLES TO DRY UP WOULD TELL YOU THAT THERE WAS WATER, AND THAT IT HAD EVAPORATED INTO THE AIR. ..BUT IT WOULD NOT TELL YOU HOW MUCH WATER!

HOWEVER... THE MYSTERY OF THE EVAPORATING VEGETABLES IS EASY TO SOLVE IF WE BUILD A MINI-SCALE AND WEIGH TINY PIECES OF VEGETABLE!

THEN WITH ONE SIMPLE BIT OF ARITHMETIC WE'LL KNOW EXACTLY HOW MUCH WATER WAS THERE!

LET'S GET STARTED! CAN I USE MY DRY INSTANT POTATOES?

OH NO!

...OF COURSE NOT! THE VEGETABLES MUST BE FRESH! INSTANT POTATOES ARE DEHYDRATED, WHICH MEANS MOST OF THEIR WATER HAS BEEN REMOVED ALREADY!

You will need:

medium weight cardboard (the kind on the back of a pad of paper would be about right)
scissors
a drinking straw

a stapler and staples
a nail, 8 cm or longer
two low glasses or egg cups exactly the same height
toothpicks
scraps of raw potato or any other raw vegetable

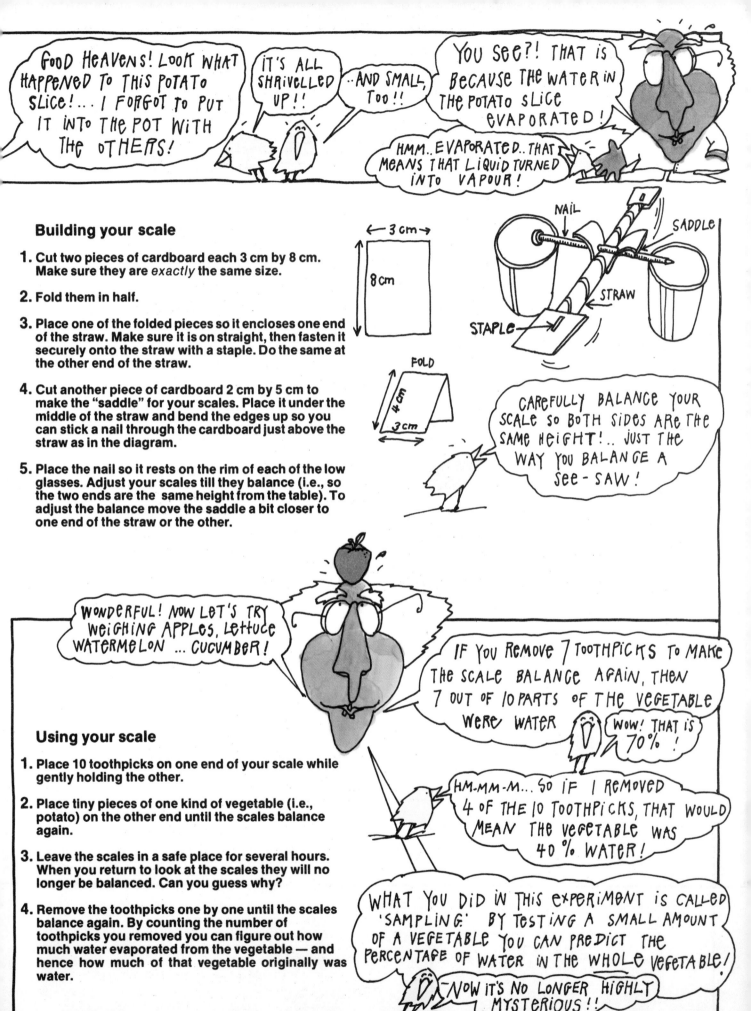

Building your scale

1. Cut two pieces of cardboard each 3 cm by 8 cm. Make sure they are *exactly* the same size.

2. Fold them in half.

3. Place one of the folded pieces so it encloses one end of the straw. Make sure it is on straight, then fasten it securely onto the straw with a staple. Do the same at the other end of the straw.

4. Cut another piece of cardboard 2 cm by 5 cm to make the "saddle" for your scales. Place it under the middle of the straw and bend the edges up so you can stick a nail through the cardboard just above the straw as in the diagram.

5. Place the nail so it rests on the rim of each of the low glasses. Adjust your scales till they balance (i.e., so the two ends are the same height from the table). To adjust the balance move the saddle a bit closer to one end of the straw or the other.

Using your scale

1. Place 10 toothpicks on one end of your scale while gently holding the other.

2. Place tiny pieces of one kind of vegetable (i.e., potato) on the other end until the scales balance again.

3. Leave the scales in a safe place for several hours. When you return to look at the scales they will no longer be balanced. Can you guess why?

4. Remove the toothpicks one by one until the scales balance again. By counting the number of toothpicks you removed you can figure out how much water evaporated from the vegetable — and hence how much of that vegetable originally was water.

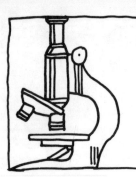

LOG:

... SCIENTIFIC, THAT IS !

HAVE YOU SEEN MY PENCIL?

?

DATE:	EXPERIMENT:

NOTES:

AUTHOR'S NOTES

Learning can be fun. Out of this philosophy came Dr. Zed and his zany team of bird friends to introduce basic science concepts.

There is more to this book than just the jokes, however. The experiments themselves have been chosen because they're fun to do and because they reward readers with interesting products that can be used or demonstrated. In every case, the efforts of Dr. Zed's readers should yield fairly spectacular results.

It is our hope that most children using this book will be able to carry out all their experiments with minimum adult supervision. To ensure this, each experiment was tried by me with the assistance of children, then further tested by the children associated with OWL, Canada's magazine for 8 to 12 year olds, where Dr. Zed is a regular feature. Thus the book is designed for use in the home as well as in the classroom. All necessary materials, therefore, have been chosen for their accessibility, and we've stressed safety throughout.

Because we also feel it is important for children to discover things for themselves, almost every experiment encourages "experimentation". By making simple adjustments or following some of our suggestions for alternatives, users of Dr. Zed should be able to invent dramatic results of their very own.

Each experiment in Dr. Zed focuses on one major science understanding, and many touch on others as well. Because most readers are at Piaget's "concrete operations" stage we encourage them to "think" through the manipulation of real objects.

A careful balance of material for each of the various science disciplines has been maintained allowing readers to discover that explorations in all these areas are equally exciting.

DEDICATION

To my wife Marion and daughters Lynda, Donna and Sandra who shared their support for this venture,
To my friend Erle,
To all the people at OWL magazine for their challenges and encouragement,
To the children who showed me the joy to be found in experimenting with everyday things. It is with them that I share equally my portion of earnings from this book through charitable organizations who care for children around the world.

— *Gordon Penrose*